A Kin/Der Owl Book Holt, Rinehart and Winston, Inc.
New York, Toronto, London

WHAT IS SOUR?

WHAT IS SWEET?

A Book of Opposites

pictures by Helen Webber

Copyright © 1967 by Holt, Rinehart and Winston, Inc.
Library of Congress Catalog Card Number AC 66-10192
Printed in the United States of America
03-085778-3

0123 60 987654321

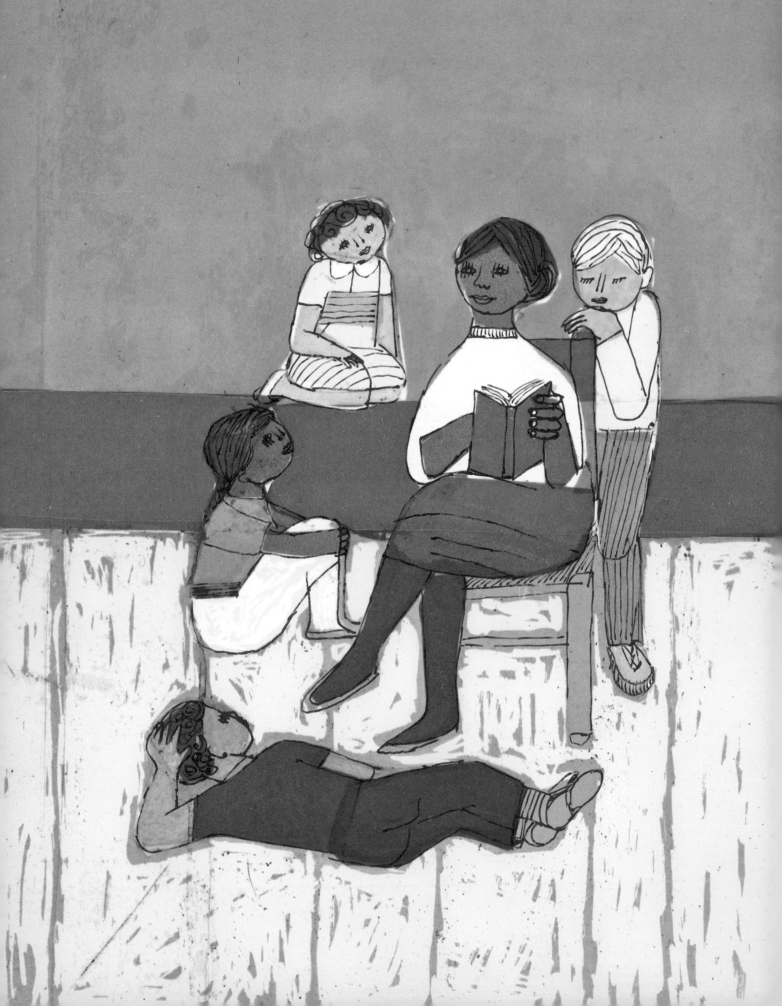

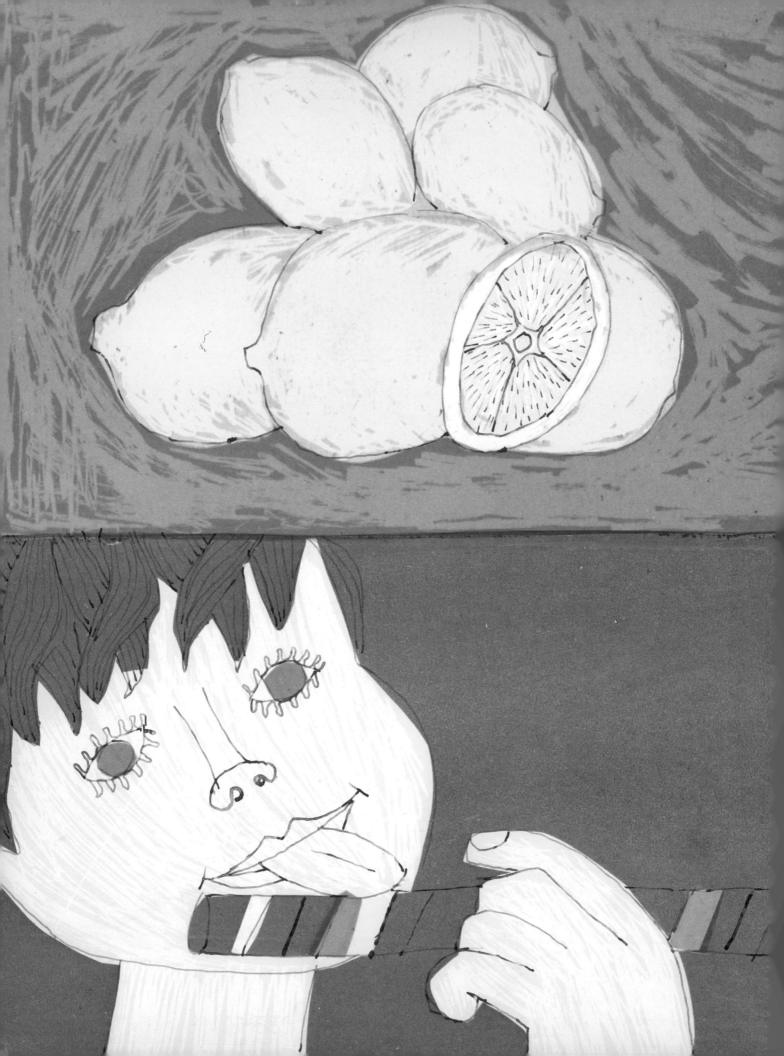